The wondrous world of
FISHES
Their Colours and Patterns

Text and photography by
Jane Burton
Produced by Ted Smart

First published in Great Britain in 1976
by Colour Library International Ltd.

Printed by I.S.G. - Vicenza
and bound by L.E.G.O. - Vicenza - Italy

Display and text filmsetting by
Focus Photoset Ltd.,
134 Clerkenwell Road, London EC1R 5DL.

ISBN 0 904681 13 0

Enquiries should be sent to:

Colour Library International Limited
80-82 Coombe Road,
New Malden, Surrey KT3 4QZ. Tel. (01) 942 7781

COLOUR LIBRARY INTERNATIONAL LIMITED

Acknowledgments

"I would like to express my thanks to John Adams, of The Ark Aquatic Centre, Bramley, Surrey, for his help"

Jane Burton

All the photographs in this book were taken by Jane Burton and are supplied by Bruce Coleman Ltd.

CONTENTS

INTRODUCTION

Fishes are among the most colourful animals in the world, rivalling birds and insects in the richness and variety of their hues. There are fishes of every colour of the spectrum, from brilliant red to palest violet. A few are unicoloured in solid blue, red or yellow, but many of the most colourful fishes are patterned in two or more colours, with spots, bands, bizarre jigsaw-shapes and apparently random splashes of brilliant and contrasting colours.

Very many of the small, active fishes in both fresh and salt water are colourful; however, their colours as we normally see them in aquaria or in flashlight photographs may be modified almost beyond recognition when the fish are viewed in their native haunts. Fish must therefore be seen under natural lighting conditions to appreciate the true significance of their colour patterns.

The modifying effect that water has on colours is dependent on the depth of water. This is because light of short wavelength (blue and violet) penetrates farther than light of longer wavelength (orange, red). In clear water, at depths of 20 metres, almost all red light and much yellow light, is filtered out, so that red and pink fish appear shades of blue-grey, and yellow fish appear lime green. Blue fish, on the other hand, may still show up brightly blue. The water of northern seas is usually coloured green by decaying plant material and by chlorophyll in minute algae. The effect of this is to filter out the shorter wavelengths. Thus deep blue light is absorbed by the greeness in the water while red light is absorbed by the water itself, with the result that green and yellow light penetrate farthest. Divers find that peacock blue and orange fish show up best in green water.

The colours of fishes are produced in two basic ways: by means of pigments, and by a peculiarity of light known as interference. Pigmentary colours are composed of chemicals contained in thousands of minute colour cells called chromatophores. These are irregular, many-lobed stars in shape and are like little bags each containing grains of a different pigment–red, orange, yellow or black. Black colour cells occur in most fishes, often scattered among other colour cells. Various combinations of colour cells give most of the reds, oranges, yellows, greens and browns. The pigment areas in the colour cells can be expanded or contracted to vary the colour tone of the fish. When the pigment areas expand, more colour shows and the fish darkens; when they contract, the fish turns pale. Red, orange and yellow pigment areas do not contract so much as the black ones. When, for instance, a red fish darkens or pales, it is often the effect of the black expanding or contracting over the red which causes the colour change.

Silver, iridescence and some blues and greens, are not produced by pigment but are interference colours.

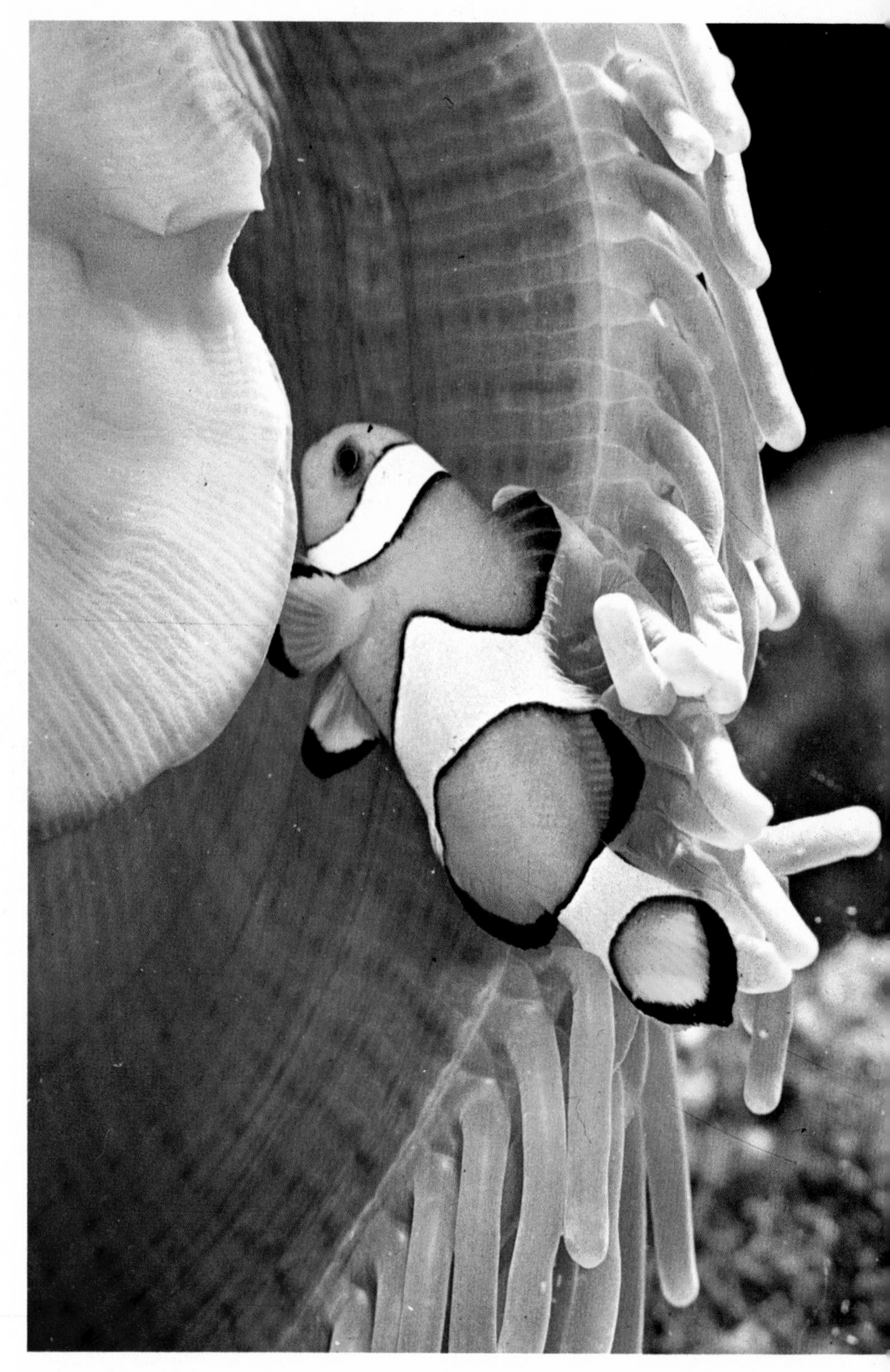

The brilliant colour pattern of the Clown Anemonefish allows it to be very conspicuous to its fellow Clowns and warns them to stay out of its territory. It can afford to risk attracting predators, to whom it must be equally conspicuous, because it rarely ventures far from the protection of its anemone.

Special cells called iridocytes carry reflective crystals of guanin. When a dense guanin-bearing layer of iridocytes occurs inside the scales, the fish appears silvery or white. When iridocytes occur outside the scales, iridescent colours are produced. These may be similar to the rainbow colours of a soap bubble or oil slick, or they may be brilliant 'electric' blue or blue-green. Rainbow iridescence is produced by the breaking up of white light into its component colours by the miriads of guanin crystals–just as sunlight is broken up by raindrops to give a rainbow. The attitude of the various facets of the guanin crystals to the observer is highly critical in producing iridescence, and so movement of an iridescent fish produces a changing pattern of colour. In just the same way a rainbow appears to 'travel' with an observer, and the position of its 'end' remains totally illusive.

Guanin crystals of a certain size and shape have the capacity to absorb all colours of the spectrum except blue, which is reflected almost totally. If black pigment cells occur behind such a guanin layer, only blue is seen: if yellow pigment is beneath, a green coloration results. 'Interference' colours of this sort often depend for maximum brilliance on the angle at which the fish is viewed. When an iridescent fish dies, its colours quickly fade due to breakdown in the alignment of the guanin crystals.

The colour and pattern of a fish is not accidental, but is the result of powerful selective forces aimed at fulfilling two basic–and often conflicting–needs: the need to be invisible to enemies or potential prey and the need to be obvious to competitors or mates. Fishes' colours have therefore come about according to which need is greatest–concealment or conspicuousness; or they may compromise ingeniously between the two. Sometimes, what may seem conspicuous to the human eye is, under natural conditions, a sophisticated form of concealment.

Many kinds of fishes that need to hide are well camouflaged and can change their colours to match their background. Some fish mimic a particular piece of their environment, such as seaweed or a dead leaf. Such fishes are not only well hidden from

ABOVE
Common Eels can change their colours to match their background by expanding or contracting the pigment areas in their black colour cells. When hiding among dark-coloured seaweed the thousands of minute black dots enlarge and the Eels turn dark. Among yellowish Knotted Wrack they become yellowish; the black dots contract allowing the yellow to show more, effectively comouflaging the fish.

BELOW
The colours of the Coral Beauty are a combination of pigments and interference colours. The orange and yellow pigments do not alter appreciably according to the light, but if the light does not catch the fish at the right angle its gorgeous blues appear merely charcoal black.

ABOVE
Blue light penetrates farthest into clear sea water, so in it deep blues and yellow stand out best. It may be for this reason that many small, active and diurnal reef fishes that need to be conspicuous are coloured blue with yellow markings, as is the Regal Tang of the Indo-Pacific.

BELOW
The African Catfish is mainly nocturnal and has only very small eyes. It probably can see little more than the difference between dark and light. Unlike diurnal fishes which live in a colourful world of sights, it lives in a world of touch and smells, aided by its long whiskery barbels.

any enemies but also from their prey. They tend to be inactive, lying about on the sea bottom or only moving with great stealth. But their camouflage means they are also hidden from their own kind, so they often have patches of bright colour on their fins. Normally they keep these folded out of sight but when another member of their own species appears they flash them to attract attention.

A fish needs to attract the attention of its own kind either to entice a mate into its territory or to warn off a competitor. Males generally are the chief territory-holders and are therefore more brightly-coloured than females. Many active, shallow-water species show very bright colours and conspicuous patterns for territorial advertisement or recognition. In the warm waters of the tropics, where fishes may breed at any season, the bright colours tend to remain constant throughout the year. In temperate climates with a marked breeding season, males assume brilliant nuptial colours only for the spawning season, reverting to cryptic self-effacing colours when there is no longer a need to maintain territories or court females.

In some fishes there is little difference between the males and females in colour or shape, although at spawning the female can usually be distinguished by her stoutness due to the eggs she is carrying. Silvery fishes that live in the open sea do not need to use colour signals to attract mates, for they often live in vast shoals. Spawning is triggered by changes in temperature and light intensity, which affect all members of the shoal alike.

Coral fishes, which are highly territorial, use their complex colour patterns to intimidate members of their own or closely related species, thus ensuring that fishes with like requirements are spread throughout the reef. The often brilliant colours also act unexpectedly as camouflage, not by merging the fish into its background but by making bits of fish stand out in startling but totally unfishy shapes. Among such fishes, the females are similar in appearance to the males and are often as territorial, defending individual space when young and shared space when paired. To distinguish mate from rival, gestures reinforce the colour signals. Gestures are possibly less important in species where males are very differently coloured from their females.

The use of colour for signalling would be ineffective if fishes' eyes were unable to distinguish colours. Nevertheless, for many years scientists were in doubt as to whether fish had true colour vision or merely saw colour as different shades of grey. Comparatively recently, however, studies have shown that many shallow-water species can perceive colours well. On the other hand, bottom-dwelling fishes living in water so deep that almost all colour is filtered out, are unable to see colours even when brought into the shallows. Also, many nocturnal or murky-water fishes that have relatively tiny eyes can only distinguish light from dark. Such fishes have other senses better developed; catfishes, for instance, live in a world of touch, feeling their way about and finding food and mates, by means of their ultra-sensitive whisker-like barbels. Such fishes, as might be expected, are not themselves colourful, being usually blackish or otherwise mud-coloured.

RIGHT
In an aquarium the silvery scales of Barbs reflect the artificial side-lighting, making them stand out very distinctly–in contrast to the effect natural top-lighting has on them in a clear pool.

Black

The black colour of fish is caused by colour cells containing the black pigment melanin, a chemical which absorbs all, or most, of the visible light. Black colour cells are called melanophores, and are the commonest type of colour cells. Yet in nature there are very few all black fish.

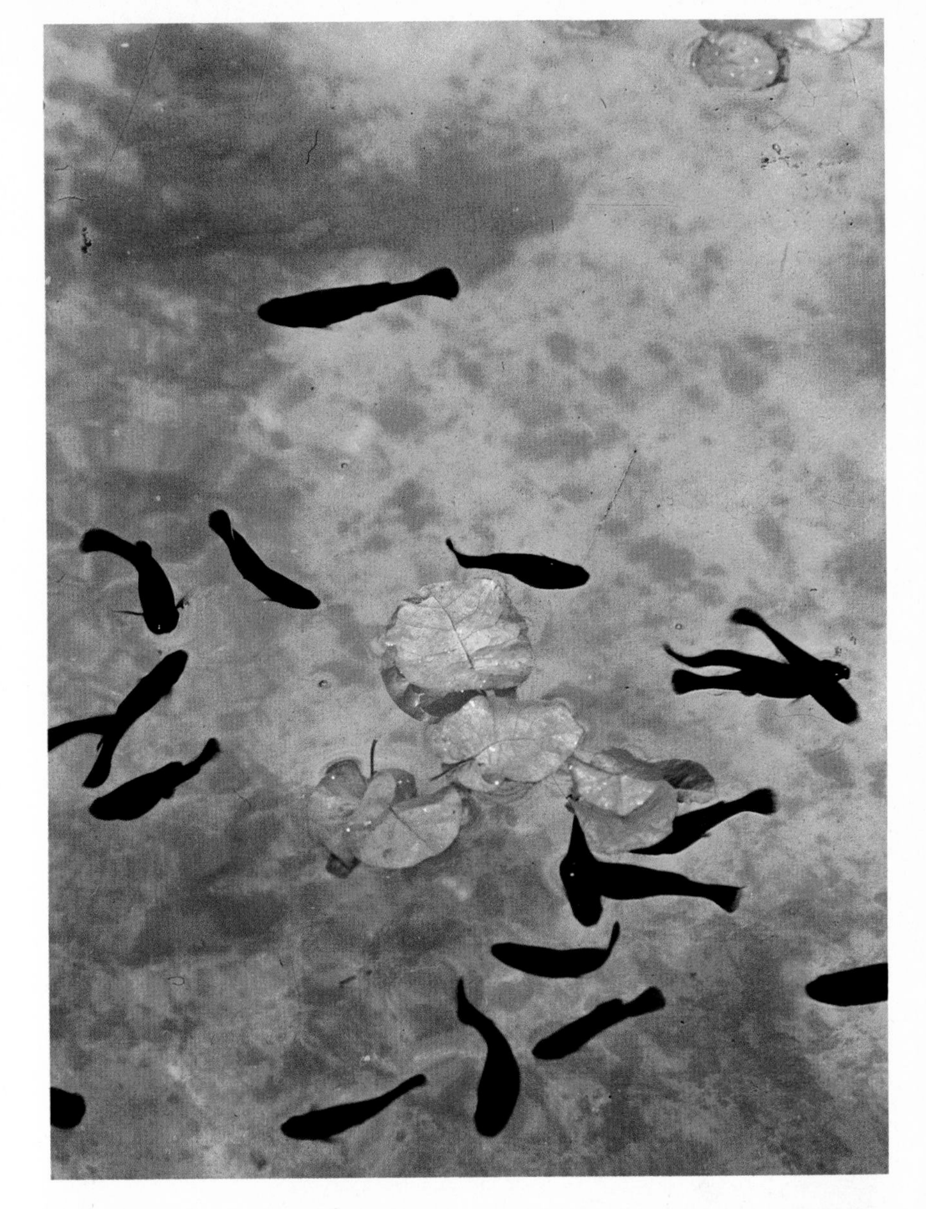

TOP RIGHT
The Black Molly is a melanic strain produced by selective breeding in aquaria. Wild Mollies vary a great deal in coloration, but are often blotched with black. Breeders, using wild fish with most black on them, eventually produced all-black varieties which breed true. Unlike the Black Shark, Black Mollies cannot vary their blackness.

BOTTOM RIGHT
The Red-tailed Black Shark is a handsome freshwater fish from Thailand. Healthy fishes are velvety-black with a contrasting blood-red tail fin. They are able to vary the intensity of their blackness: frightened fishes change fairly rapidly from black to light grey.

LEFT
The black Angelfish is another melanic variety produced under domestication. This is the Black-lace Veiltail. The dark fins and body are set off by the red of the eye, which has been retained from the wild coloration (see pp 5 & 43).

Red

Red is not a common colour among fishes because it cannot be seen underwater as red except very close to the surface. Water, however clear, quickly filters out red light, making red fishes appear black and pink fishes grey. It is probably for this reason that there are few diurnal reef fishes coloured red. Bright red in fishes is caused mainly by pigments known as carotenoids, so called because one of them, carotene, is found in carrots. Fishes are unable to make carotenoids for themselves; they must get them from their food, particularly such small crustacea as shrimps. Shrimps cannot make carotenoids either; they obtain them by feeding on tiny plants which are able to make them from chemicals in the water. Colour cells that contain carotenoids are called erythrophores.

ABOVE
Bright brick-red is one of the domesticated forms produced by breeders from the wild Mexican Platy. Like the Swordtail and the various Mollies, the Platy is now bred in many colours and with varied fin-forms.

BELOW
Squirrelfishes have large eyes and pink to red coloration. They are nocturnal, hiding by day in caves and coming out at night to feed on smaller fish and shrimps. Their redness makes them invisible under natural lighting conditions, partly because they stay in the dark but also because the red wavelength of light does not penetrate far into the water. In the sea, even in the daytime, their redness is equivalent to black, and their pink to grey-blue.

LEFT
The Rosy Barb is one of the most beautiful small Barbs. Outside the breeding season males and females have shining olive-green backs and silvery bellies tinged with pink. At spawning time the male becomes a glittering ink-red.

Identity Marks

Red is used by many kinds of freshwater fishes in identity marks, usually as spots of colour about the eye or as red on fins or tail. These marks help a fish to recognise another member of its own species, and assist pairs to come together for spawning.

TOP RIGHT
Tinfoil Barbs, one of the larger Barbs of South-east Asia, develop brilliant carmine on the fins and eyes as they mature. Young fishes have more silvery sides and yellow fins (p 9).

RIGHT
West African Red-eyed Characins are fishes of forest waterways. Like the two Neon Characins of South American forest pools (p 28) they have some red on them and a broad shining band which can flash iridescent rainbow-coloured in the sun.

ABOVE
The red on the eye of the Angelfish is the only bright spot of colour about this elegant South American Cichlid. Its eye appears to be a typical fish eye, with round pupil set fairly immobile on the side of the head. It is much like the eye of any other vertebrate in structure, but adapted to cope with the special problems of seeing underwater. Of necessity somewhat shortsighted, it is specially able to see movement and has good discrimination of colour, but is not so good at seeing the shape of objects. (For whole fish see pp 5 and 43).

ABOVE RIGHT
White Cloud Mountain Minnows live in shoals in the gorges of the White Cloud Mountains in China. The young are even more colourful than the adult, with a more prominent iridescent band as well as the red on tail and fins.

BOTTOM RIGHT
The most conspicuous difference between these two very similar 'Blood Tetras', the Rosy and the Bleeding Heart, is that the latter has a red blotch on the flank and red on the eye.

Orange

Orange colours of fish are caused by the same group of pigments, the carotenoids, that give red and yellow fishes their colours. As with other pigmentary colours the intensity of orange coloration depends on the density of the colour cells and on the amount of pigment granules in each cell.

TOP
The Rock Beauty when young is intensely orange, but as it grows so does the area of black on its sides, and its coloration decreases to yellow with red on the fins–as if the primary colours were separating out. Its blue eye remains constant throughout life.

CENTRE
The orange coloration of the Malaysian freshwater Harlequin Fish hardly bears comparison with the orange of some tropical marine fishes. Nonetheless this is a very pretty little fish, with its orange flanks set off by a blue-black wedge and iridescent back.

BOTTOM
The Clown Rasbora is another Malaysian Rasbora with a delicate orange coloration, set off in this case by two blue-black blotches. Like the Harlequin it is a shoaling species and very peaceful. The male, above, has two White Spot cysts on his tail fin.

RIGHT
The Corkwing is the most commonly seen Wrasse of northern Europe, in shore pools or amongst seaweed below tide mark. Females are dull mottled brown, but males are red-brown spotted with green, with orange and iridescent blue bars on the gill covers –orange being the colour that stands out best in green northern waters, according to skin-divers' observations.

Golden

Very occasionally in the wild a beautiful golden individual of a common species has been seen; this is a rare orange or yellow mutation from the normal colour. Under domesticity, many kinds of fishes can be bred to produce golden strains.

LEFT
The Goldfish was developed by the Chinese from golden forms of an Asiatic wild carp at least a thousand years ago. Young Goldfish are brown, much like their wild ancestors, becoming golden only when they have reached about 1½ inches in length and under warm conditions. Selective breeding has produced delicate and bizarre forms with fan tails, shortened bodies and enlarged eyes. (See also p2).

TOP
The original home of the Common Carp was also Asia, but today it is distributed throughout the whole of Europe as well. Its wild colours are much like those of the wild Goldfish. Domesticated Carp of many colours, including golden, red, blue and white, have been selectively bred by the Japanese.

BELOW
A golden form of the Silver Orfe occurs naturally in various places in south Germany. Here, almost all young Silver Orfe metamorphose into Golden Orfe at a certain age.

ABOVE
The Tench, too, produces golden colour varieties which can be a beautiful yellow or orange, with the body and fins occasionally spotted brown. Young wild-coloured Tench are brassy green (p 20).

BELOW
Not only hardy cold-water species have been bred in golden varieties. The warmth-loving Golden Sail-fin Molly has the red pupils of an albino, but retains some of the lovely red and blue spots of the wild fish (p 23).

Yellow

Many reef fishes have a great deal of yellow about them. Blue and yellow are the most conspicuous colours in the blue waters of coral seas, but yellow underwater does not appear the same by natural lighting as it does when lit by flashlight–it combines with the blueness of the water to look lime-green. Reef fishes with much yellow on them can afford to be permanently conspicuous: they do not need to stalk their prey since they feed on algae or small animals on the coral, and they are never far from crevices into which they can dart to escape a predator.

TOP RIGHT
Many Butterflyfishes are predominantly yellow, but all have some distinguishing spot or stripe to differentiate the species. The Addis has a blue-grey triangular cheek patch and a black line on the hind edge of the dorsal fin. This helps to keep closely-related species separate because no other Butterflyfish is considered by the Addis for a mate unless it is the exact shade of yellow with the exact fin-line and cheek patch.

CENTRE RIGHT
The Yellow Longnose Butterflyfish has a forceps-like snout for probing tiny holes in the coral and extracting the animals living in them. It presents roughly the same yellow shape as the Addis, but is immediately distinguishable from it by means of the black spot on the ventral fin and the dark 'highwayman's mask'.

BOTTOM RIGHT
The Yellow Sailfin Tang is unusual in being entirely yellow, with no spots or pattern of other colours and no attempt to hide its eye. When alarmed it raises its dorsal fin. This gives it a 'surprised' expression to us, analagous to our raised eyebrows. But from a predatory fish's point of view the Tang's shape is then so different to the 'normal' fish shape that it may delay its pounce, giving the Tang a vital split second to disappear.

LEFT
Streamlining for speed was not a consideration that determined the shape of the Seahorse. But its strange form and prehensile tail suit it to a rather sedentary life among seaweed or coral growths. The beautiful yellow of this large species from the Indo-Pacific is seen only when the fish is happily settled. Newly imported fish are dull blackish, the gold may take a month or more to reappear.

Green

So many fishes live among green aquatic plants that it is surprising to find how very few are actually coloured green. Green in animals can be caused by blue-reflecting crystals over yellow pigment cells, or by a mixture of yellow cells among black cells. The green plant pigment, chlorophyll, cannot be used by animals as a means of colouring.

ABOVE
The Bronze Armoured Catfish has bony armour on the head and bony plates on the flanks overlapping like tiles on a roof. In different lights the strong metallic glint on this armour-plating shines sometimes coppery, sometimes golden, often green. These little Catfishes live in slow-flowing, sometimes stagnant waters, grubbing about the bottom with their sensitive barbels.

CENTRE
This small Caribbean reef fish is an aquatic version of the chameleon, coloured basically green but capable of varying that colour to blend with the alga-covered rocks or seaweed among which it lives.

BELOW
The Tench lives among thick growths of water weed in Europe's lakes. Young fish are a beautiful bronzy green, big fish blacken with age. This young fish is feeding by scooping up mouthfuls of mud, swallowing any small creatures therein, then spitting the mud out again.

Blue

There may be a blue pigment which is responsible for the coloration of some marine fishes, but in most fishes blue is an interference effect caused in the same way as the blueness of the sky and the blue of a kingfisher's feathers. Minute crystals of guanin in the fish's skin reflect in all directions, or 'scatter', blue light more than red light. Behind the scattering layer is a black background. The result is blue reflected light known as Tyndall blue.

ABOVE
The underwater world of the coral reef is predominantly blue, because the blue wavelenghts of light penetrate deepest. In blue light, deep blue and yellow are conspicuous, and many reef fishes such as the Blue-faced Angelfish are patterned in these colours.

RIGHT
The medium-tone blue of the Powder-blue Surgeonfish may be a form of camouflage. Against the background of the reef it is clearly visible, but here is within easy reach of sheltering corals should danger threaten. When it leaves the safety of the coral to feed in open water, its blueness melts into the blue-ness all around it.

RIGHT
The male Siamese Fighting Fish is renowned not only for his fighting fervour but for his beauty. However, all the lovely blues, reds, purples and greens of aquarium fish have been selectively bred; wild Fighters, though very variable in colour, are generally predominantly red-brown.

LEFT
The Blue Gourami is also a domesticated strain, bred from the Three-spot Gourami; wild fish are olive-coloured. There is also a golden strain in which the two spots have almost disappeared from flank and tail. (The eye makes the third 'spot' in the blue and wild forms).

CENTRE
The Electric-blue Damselfish stands out brilliantly against pale coral polyps and an orange Helmet shell. But a predatory fish looking out from among the corals and seeing the Damsel against the blueness of the open water, would not find the little fish so conspicuous.

BELOW
Among freshwater fishes blue often occurs as a galaxy of bright spots rather than a solid blue. The Jack Dempsey, a notably pugnacious Cichlid of the Amazon Basin, is spangled all over with blue spots which intensify to a brilliant deep dark blue in the breeding season.

CENTRE RIGHT
The male Sailfin Molly has a truly magnificent dorsal fin which he flashes in aggressive display at another male and in courtship of a female. Both fin and body are blue-spotted, so under full sail he must appear nearly three times his normal size.

LOWER
The Blue-spotted Argus or Jewel Grouper is spattered all over with electric-blue dots. Like all groupers it feeds in midwater on anything it can snap up. It can vary its background colour from chocolate to black, and the intensity of its spots according to its mood.

Purple

The purple colours of some fishes are again interference colours and are produced, like most blues, by a Tyndall scattering from minute particles of guanin in the skin or scales. All but the shortest wavelengths of light are absorbed, giving a violet reflection. However, while blues are common among tropical marine fishes, purple appears to be a rare colour.

LEFT
The Royal Gramma of the Caribbean is brilliantly-coloured, even by reef-fish standards. It swims with its belly close to coral or rock, so that at times it is head up, at others head down, or even, under an overhang, upside-down.

BELOW
The Lilac Snapper grows fairly large, and like any snapper is extremely voracious. Its pale violet coloration possibly acts like the blue of the Powder-blue Surgeon as a camouflage to the fish when out hunting away from the reef.

Silver

The silver colour of many fishes is produced not by colour cells but by reflecting cells or iridocytes. These contain crystals of guanin, making them opaque and able to reflect light. In silvery fishes the iridocytes are inside the scales in a layer called the argenteum. It is this layer that gives the fishes their silvery or white appearance.

ABOVE
The Silver Shark is a beautifully-streamlined mid-water swimmer–not a true shark, of course, but somewhat shark-shaped with its high dorsal fin. Such silvery fishes may have so much guanin in their scales that it can be collected and used to make artificial pearls.

RIGHT
Monos, also known as Fingerfish or Malayan Angels, have small scales but nonetheless very silvery sides that reflect the light in varying intensity according to the angle at which they are swimming.

Albinos

Albino fishes lack all pigment in their skins. Their eyes are coloured deep pink by the tiny blood vessels at the back of the iris and their bodies are pale pink where blood vessels show through the skin. Albinos probably do not survive long in the wild, for they are too conspicuous.

TOP LEFT
Albino Swordtails lack pigment in the skin but have a little iridescence on the flanks which gives them a translucent, delicate appearance.

TOP RIGHT
The Phantom variety of the Siamese Fighting Fish is a delicate cream colour. This fish is not a true albino, for there is some black pigment retained on the pectoral fins and gill-covers, and in the pupil of the eye. The male Siamese Fighter builds a bubble raft at the surface in which he cares for the eggs and fry.

CENTRE LEFT
The albino Catfish is coloured a fairly strong pink by the red oxygen-carrying pigment, haemoglobin, in the blood. Possibly this is a more pleasing colour than the normal, which can accurately be described as muddy (p 8).

BOTTOM RIGHT
The Kissing Gourami is rarely seen in its wild greenish-silver colours outside its native Malaysia. This is an unpigmented variety, uniform pink with a pearly sheen on the flanks, the only pigment being in the black eyes. 'Kissing' is probably a form of mild aggression between males, rather than courtship behaviour.

BOTTOM LEFT
The Blind Cave Characin is one of the few true cave-dwelling fishes. It lives in total darkness in underground pools and streams in Mexico. It has lost all pigment from the skin, and its eyes have degenerated to pinheads overgrown with skin. But it makes up for loss of sight by heightened senses of touch and smell.

Iridescence

Iridescence is produced like silver by the iridocytes. When iridocytes are inside the scales, the effect is silver or white. When the iridocytes are outside the scales they produce an iridescence because the microscopic guanin crystals break down light into its component colours. The colour of the fish is determined by the precise arrangement of the crystals, which absorb some colours and reflect others. Movement of an iridescent fish can produce a change of colours.

TOP
Quite a few species of fish that live in forest or jungle waters show iridescence. The Congo Tetra is a forest species from the Zaire (Congo) Basin. In dim light, such as filters through the canopy of trees, it shows brilliant blue, green and golden iridescence.

CENTRE
The blue iridescent stripes of the Cardinal Tetra and other 'neons' vary in intensity according to the angle and amount of light catching them–they flash conspicuously at the surface or glow richly when the fishes dive–an effective disappearing act from aerial fish-eaters.

BELOW
Like the Cardinal, the Neon Tetra is found in jungle watercourses at the headwaters of the Amazon. These two inch-long Characins are considered the most beautiful and jewel-like of freshwater fishes.

Camouflage

The coloration of many kinds of fishes is designed to make them as unobtrusive as possible. Concealing colours, or camouflage, can either be protective, hiding a fish from predators; or aggressive, hiding it from its prey. Often camouflage serves both purposes, for many small fishes prey on even smaller fishes, and very few are so big and powerful that they themselves are immune from predation.

RIGHT
Many otherwise quite colourful fishes are very well camouflaged from above. Guppies in a mangrove swamp are at risk from herons and kingfishers, but can adjust the brightness and colour of their backs to match the dim light coming up from below. When seen from above they match the brown mud of the sunlit swamp.

Cryptic Colours

Constant attack by predators has caused some fish to evolve cryptic colours that give them remarkable camouflage.

TOP RIGHT
Cryptic coloration, to be effective, depends largely on the immobility of the wearer. The camouflage of the Long-spined Sea Scorpion has a two-fold advantage when it is motionless on seaweedy rocks: it protects it from its enemies and hides it from potential prey. Small fishes, prawns and crabs are unaware of its presence until too late.

CENTRE
The Freshwater Pufferfish of South-east Asia lives in brackish waters and swamps. Its complicated pattern of golden squiggles and rings blends well with submerged palms and fallen mangrove leaves when the fish rests motionless on the bottom. When disturbed, these same markings become conspicuous and may act as a warning, for the fish can give a sharp bite with its parrot-like beak, and its flesh is not only unpalatable but poisonous.

LEFT
Any fish, such as the Rock Goby, blends best with its surroundings when its colouring reproduces the colours, shapes and texture of its background. Light and dark browns with haphazard spots and mottling break up the fishy shape and merge it into almost any natural environment of rocks and plants.

BELOW
The European Stone Loach lives in fast-flowing streams or lake shallows. It prefers a pebbly bottom where its yellow-brown back with darker spotted flanks merges well with gravel. However, among waterlogged willow leaves its camouflage is just as effective, its shape as well as colour blending with that of the leaves.

Flatfishes

The flatfishes are masters of camouflage and can change their colour to match their background. The black colour cells in their skin are under very good control, so that when the fish lands on a patch of sand its eyes register a pale tone and the black pigment areas contract to give its upperside a stippled, sandy appearance. When settled on a dark rock, the pigment areas expand and the fish turns dark; on blotchy gravel it becomes blotched light and dark to match.

TOP LEFT
The flattened body of the Plaice merges so well with the seabed it casts no perceptible shadow. It can not only change its colour to match its background, be it mud, sand or gravel, but when it comes to rest it rapidly undulates its fins, throwing up some of the substrate onto itself for further camouflage. This effectively masks the orange spots on its back, which are otherwise very conspicuous underwater.

CENTRE
Large Flounders live in deep water, young ones inhabit the tidal zone and often feed in estuaries, especially during the summer. Most of the day they lie buried in the sand with just the eyes protruding. At night they emerge to feed.

BELOW LEFT
The Topknot is one of the smaller North Sea flatfishes, living on stony or rocky ground in the seaweed zone. Like other Flatfishes, it is practically invisible until it moves. When seriously alarmed it darts away, then, instantly still, seems to disappear again as if by magic.

RIGHT
Like all Flatfishes, the Topknot began life as a normal, symmetrical, upright-swimming larva. During the course of its development it started to swim on one side. At the same time, one eye moved over the top of the head and onto the other side of the body. The fish then settled on the seabed, blind side down. The upper, eyed side became pigmented, the blind underside remained colourless except where the internal organs and spinal cord shine through dark pink.

Disguise

Disguise is an advanced form of camouflage in which the shape and colour of an animal copies a particular piece of its environment. Among insects and frogs there are very many that mimic leaves, flowers, twigs or bark to a remarkable degree; but among fishes only a few actually mimic plants rather than simply blend with them.

TOP RIGHT
The Pike is a long slim predatory fish with a large mouth and formidable dentition. A yearling Pike, or pikerel, has dark bars on its side which mimic the fine leaves of waterweed, while its pale dorsal stripe represents the plant's stem. This pikerel is 'pointing' the dorsal fin of a gudgeon which it saw move among the pondweed. The gudgeon is nearly as big as the pikerel, more suitable prey for a grown pike.

BOTTOM RIGHT
The Worm Pipefish is indeed wormy, in shape, size and movement, but not in colour. A relative of the Seahorses, it mimics the blackish bootlace stems of wrack and thongweed among which it twines.

LEFT
The Caribbean Dwarf Angler or Frogfish is covered with weed-like growths of skin which perfectly mimic a clump of seaweed. On its snout is a fishing rod with a convincing 'worm' on the end which the Frogfish dangles seductively in front of potential prey to lure them within gulping range. Its better-known relative the Sargassumfish is similarly covered with weedy growths which mimic the floating Sargassum weed in which it lives.

Dead Leaves

The commonest disguise among freshwater fishes is to mimic dead leaves.

LEFT
The most remarkable leaf-mimics are the aptly-named Leaf Fishes. The Siamese Leaf-fish is typical of the group. Its flattened body and pointed snout mimic a leaf shape, and its mottled brown coloration suggests mould patches on a waterlogged dead leaf. The tail fin, which might spoil the line of the 'leaf', is transparent.

BELOW
The Butterfly fish of West Africa hangs motionless at the surface like a small cluster of dead leaves and plant debris. It feeds chiefly on insects that fall on the water, but can also leap out and catch them on the wing by spreading its large pectoral fins and gliding a short way.

ABOVE
Marbled Hatchetfishes hang at the surface of forest pools, back to back with their reflections when seen from below. Their deep pectoral keel and brown mottling give them a floating dead-leaf appearance. To escape attack they flip out of the water by beating their pectoral fins and can actually fly for short distances.

BELOW RIGHT
The South American Leaf-fish lurks motionless among vegetation. When a small fish such as a Guppy swims near, it drifts within striking distance propelled by almost invisible movements of its transparent hind fins. With a sucking gulp it swallows a small fish faster than the human eye can follow.

Countershading

Very few fishes are the same colour or tone all over. Most are darker on the back shading to very pale on the belly. This is known as countershading. Since sunlight mostly strikes the water from above, a unicoloured fish seen from the side would appear lightest on the back with a dark shadow underneath, and would be very solid-looking and conspicuous to a predator. The dark back and light belly of a countershaded fish counteract the light and shadow and have the effect of making the fish appear flat. Enemies have more difficulty in identifying an apparently flat shape as something actually round and therefore most likely edible.

ABOVE LEFT
The importance of countershading in camouflage is emphasized by the Sleeper Goby which habitually rests or even cruises along upsidedown. It is capable of a wide range of colour changes, from almost black to very pale with a dark horizontal line. When upsidedown, it becomes darker on the belly than on the back, like the Upsidedown Catfish of Africa, a better known example of reversed countershading.

BELOW
Two small Roach are here viewed so that one of them can be seen simultaneously from above and from the side. The typical colours of countershading – dark grey back shading gradually to a pale belly – are well illustrated.

Glass Fishes

Glass fishes have achieved the next best thing to invisibility by becoming almost so. Their tissues are transparent as glass, so that background plants are visible through their bodies.

ABOVE
Young Siamese Glassfishes are pale yellow and transparent, with the spine and swim bladder clearly visible. The abdominal cavity has a silvery covering which is thought to prevent the growth of algae in the gut by reflecting light outwards.

RIGHT
The skeleton of the Glass Catfish is clearly visible as if by X-ray, but when resting the fish positions itself obliquely with the tail down, so that the backbone repeats the angle of the leaves' midribs. This species is among the very few Catfishes that live in mid-water; the majority grub about on the bottom.

Mirror-camouflage

The most sophisticated form of camouflage is found in the silvery fishes. It works in conjunction with counter-shading and is known as mirror-camouflage. In open water, light from all horizontal directions is about equal in colour and intensity. The image seen in a mirror hung there and viewed horizontally will therefore be much the same as the background, making the mirror almost invisible. Although silvery fishes are often to some extent laterally flattened, their flanks are gently curved, and so cannot act directly as flat mirrors. However, the myriads of tiny guanin crystals beneath the scales are so arranged that, even on the more curved surfaces towards the belly, they reflect light horizontally, and the whole fish functions almost as a vertical mirror. When viewed from the side in open water whole shoals of fish look totally unsubstantial and seem to melt into the blueness or green around them – an almost perfect camouflage.

TOP RIGHT
The silvery sides of the Bass reflect the greenish light of the North Sea and tend to camouflage the fish, although its dorsal fins, here raised in a defensive gesture, catch the light and stand out clearly.

BOTTOM RIGHT
Mirror-camouflage only works from the side. Viewed from below, even silvery Grey Mullet will always appear as dark silhouettes when swimming against the light.

LEFT
For perfect camouflage, silvery fishes such as these South American Characins must hold the correct position in the water, for once they tilt, brilliant light is reflected from their sides. Such reflections may be used in self-defence: a shoal of silver fishes dashing hither and thither could well confuse a predator with its dazzling multiple flashes of light.

Vertical Stripes

In addition to countershading and mirror-camouflage, many fishes have disruptive vertical stripes, dark lines on a light ground or white bars on dark. Stripes have the effect of breaking up the outline of the fish, allowing it to blend into the general pattern of vertical brightness and shadows among the leaves and stems of aquatic plants.

RIGHT
The black and silver striping of the Angelfish allows it to merge with its background to a surprising extent. The dark stripes can be intensified to deepest black or faded to pale grey, according to the mood or needs of the individual.

LEFT
The Discus is another large and elegant Cichlid which moves in a stately fashion through the jungle of underwater vegetation. Again, this fish's vertical stripes can be lightened or intensified and are good camouflage in a slow-moving species living among plants.

BOTTOM LEFT
The Flame Dwarf Angelfish is a gorgeous reef-dweller from Hawaii. Its shiny orange sides are set off by black vertical bars and deep blue on the fins, which serve to break up its shape and confuse would-be predators.

BELOW
The Chocolate Gourami is a very delicate species found in Malaysia and Sumatra. A fine dark chocolate on the back with white or yellow banding, it merges well among the shadows and streaks of sunlight.

Horizontal Stripe

A dark horizontal stripe has a camouflaging effect in a similar way to vertical stripes. It breaks up the shape of the fish, destroys its symmetry and blends with the lines of leaves and stems.

TOP LEFT
The silvery-white and black Penguin Fish swims with tail down, so that when a small shoal is hovering among water plants the very strong diagonals have a disruptive and camouflaging effect.

BELOW
Golden gleaming scales make the European Minnow a quite beautiful small fish. Its colour varies according to the condition of the fish: sometimes pale with vague transverse bars, more often dark. In the breeding season males develop a scarlet breast and white tubercles on the head.

Dazzle Stripes

Just as the mirror sides of silvery fishes can confuse an attacking predator by flashing brilliant reflections on and off, so contrasting dazzle stripes can have a similar bewildering effect.

ABOVE
A contrast in stripes is seen in these Amazon Tetras. Under natural lighting conditions the silvery sides of the Black Widows would disappear and their vertical stripes merge with the background of water plants; while the iridescent dazzle stripes of the Neons and Black Neon flicker as the fish dart about the pool.

CENTRE
Glowlight Tetras have a brilliant band of orange, which in fresh water is the colour that stands out most conspicuously against green plants and green water. Like the blue stripes of the Neons, these orange stripes darting here and there could well confuse a predator and spoil its aim.

BELOW LEFT
The Zebra Fish, like the mammal after which it is named, is boldly striped in black and white. A shoal of striped fishes dashing about could well deflect a predator's aim. In addition, like the Zebra's stripes, the fish's may be a form of countershading, conspicuous close-to but camouflaging when the black and white appears to merge into grey through distance or dim lighting.

BELOW RIGHT
Sometimes a colour pattern that makes an individual fish stand out at close quarters causes it to merge into its background when at a distance. The black and white stripes break up the fishes' contours and become a camouflage, as in this Striped Drum.

Spots

Whether a fish is black spotted white, or pale spotted dark, its spots may be used as camouflage, either by causing it to merge with its background or by breaking up its outline to confuse its enemies.

LEFT
Young Scats, or Argus Fish, are often brightly coloured, with bold jet-black spots on a silvery body, and yellow or red fins. With age, these colours darken.

TOP RIGHT
The Smooth Trunkfish is unusual among fishes in having an armoured body. Hexagonal bony plates in the skin are fused together to make a rigid casing in which only the eyes, fins and jaws can move. This fish is an untouchable, for when threatened it secretes poisonous substances into the water. Moreover, it is well camouflaged, for unlike the leopard it can change its spots, to become lighter or darker to match its background.

CENTRE RIGHT
The Sucking Catfish is one of the hill-stream fishes that live in fast little mountain streams. It sucks onto stones against the current, and rasps algae off the bottom with its ventral sucking mouth. At night or on a dark bottom it appears nearly black; on pale pebbles in the daytime it lightens its colour to match.

BOTTOM RIGHT
Young Brown Trout have a distinctive line of up to thirteen dark 'finger-prints' along the side. These are the parr marks, which disappear as the fish grows, giving way to a scattering of handsome black and red spots rimmed with blue. Even baby trout are highly territorial, chasing off others that hover too close to their 'station', which they maintain by swimming into the current only fast enough to stay in the same place.

Disruptive Coloration

Most fishes are good at seeing movement and colour, but not so good at distinguishing shapes. The bold contrasting colours and patterns of reef fishes therefore are a disruptive coloration; they act as a kind of camouflage by breaking up the outline of a fish and creating an optical illusion of multiple unfishlike creatures.

TOP LEFT
The Brown-faced Butterflyfish lacks the yellows of other marine Butterflies but its quiet colours are nonetheless pleasing. Its typical Butterflyfish shape is broken up into three distinct and unrelated shapes, each more conspicuous than the fish itself.

BOTTOM LEFT
The young of several species of marine Angelfishes are boldly coloured in black and blue overlaid with a striking pattern of bright stripes to break up their simple, easily distinguishable form. The young French Angelfish is jet black with yellow stripes, but as he grows he turns into a dull-coloured grey adult.

RIGHT
In many coralfishes the body outline is further broken up by extending the already disruptive markings into the fins. The Wimple Fish, also known as the Pennant Coralfish, has a long dorsal fin which extends its central white stripe and carries it back diagonally, disguising the fish's true shape.

Eye-masks

Much of the effectiveness of any disruptive colour pattern depends on also concealing the eyes. As in many other animals, a fish's eye can be its most conspicuous feature. Therefore, to conceal the staring round black pupil the fish may wear a disruptive eye-mask. The mask appears to be a whole unit, but is composed of a black ocular band above and below the eye, while black markings on the eye itself link the band through the pupil, so that not only is the eye concealed, but its movements are also.

BELOW
The Rainbow (top) is perhaps the loveliest of the Butterflyfishes, the Pearlscale (middle) and the Golden (lower) among the most striking. Black eye-masks are one of the most conspicuous features of these fishes, but they conceal the eye rather than accentuate it, and also help to break up the fishy shape.

ABOVE
The Striped Sailfin Tang looks in shape and seems to behave much like the Yellow Sailfin (p 19). It is hard to know what factor determined that one should be plain yellow with a conspicuous eye, while the other is disruptively striped with its eye masked. When the behaviour of reef fishes becomes better known, this puzzle may be solved.

RIGHT
When a fish is patterned with vertical stripes, as is this Regal Angelfish, it is usually found that one of the stripes runs through the eye, or a smaller one each side of it to give the same masking effect.

Eye-spots

Many eye-masked fishes have conspicuous false eyes on the dorsal fin or near the tail-base, usually a black circular spot surrounded by a light ring. The eye-spot is nearly always much larger than the true eye and may mislead a predator into presuming that the wearer is very much bigger than it really is. Or it may cause the predator to attack from the wrong angle, enabling the eye-spotted fish to dart away in an unexpected direction.

TOP LEFT
The Long-nosed or Copper Band Butterflyfish masks its eyes with another copper stripe rather than a black one. The larger black eye-spot on its dorsal fin is therefore much more conspicuous than is its real eye. The forceps snout is used to suck small animals such as shrimps out of holes in the coral.

TOP RIGHT
The Majestic Snapper is one of the larger reef fishes and very predatory. Probably the conspicuous eye-spot near the base of its tail is for the purpose of deflecting attacks of the small Sabre-toothed Blenny that darts from coral crannies to bite chunks from the soft skin around the eyes of larger fishes. (See Cleaner Wrasse p 58).

CENTRE
The Butterfish or Gunnel lives in the seaweed zone around the coast of northern Europe. It has 9-13 eye-spots along the base of the dorsal fin, and its inconspicuous eye is masked by a brown line. A bite out of the fin or even the back is not seriously disabling to a fish, for wounds heal and fins regenerate.

BOTTOM LEFT
Spiny Eels have little in common with true Eels except a similarity of form. They hide by day deep among the weeds and mud with only snout and eyes visible. In the evening they emerge to feed. The conspicuous eye-spots, unusual in a freshwater fish, are probably used in courtship displays, as well as for predator-diversion.

BOTTOM RIGHT
Small black spots on the head of the Twin-spot Wrasse camouflage the real eyes, while on the dorsal fin two large black eye-spots, accentuated by red patches, divert a predator's attention towards the tail, allowing the Wrasse to dive head first into the sand to escape.

Warning Coloration

Among insects, a bold coloration of black and yellow stripes is a warning signal that the wearer is poisonous. It is so effective and well-understood that some harmless insects wear the same pattern and deceive predators into leaving them alone. It is tempting to think that bold black and orange stripes among fishes is a warning coloration, but it is more likely to be another example of disruptive patterning.

TOP LEFT
The Tiger Barb is a peaceful though very active little fish, with no spines or hidden poison. When unmolested it dashes about conspicuously in mid-water, but once alarmed its stripes become an effective camouflage as it hides among the plants.

RIGHT
The colours of the Regal Scorpionfish could be genuine warning colours. The whole fish is strikingly patterned in red, black, pink and white, and it has enormous ornamented fins which it spreads menacingly if molested. Its self-confident behaviour shows total disregard for predators – justifiably, for its dorsal spines can inject a lethal venom. (See also p 1).

CENTRE ABOVE
Clown Loaches are the most colourful of their family, and it would be easy to jump to the conclusion that their colours were a warning to other fishes not to touch them. Like other loaches, they have a sickle-like barb just in front of the eye which they unsheath when attacked. They are very sociable fishes and will shoal with other species, such as the Tiger Barb, that have the same colours.

BOTTOM LEFT
The Sumatran Bumblebee Goby is small in size and unobtrusive in behaviour, living mostly on the bottom in slightly brackish waters. Despite its name and waspy stripes it has no barbs, poison or sting. Even in an aquarium it is surprisingly difficult to spot unless actively swimming.

BOTTOM RIGHT
Coolie Loaches are much more eel-like than the Clowns, but in other respects typical Loaches. They too have an erectile barb in front of the eye. However, there are other spiky fishes, such as the Stickleback (p 60), which predators quickly learn to leave alone without the help of a warning coloration.

Seasonal Colour Changes

During the breeding season the males of many freshwater species become very much more brightly coloured. They need to be as conspicuous as possible to other members of their own species–to other males, to warn them to keep away; to females, to encourage spawning. The actual mechanism of seasonal colour change is often complex, involving control by the nervous system and by hormones. This colour change takes place slowly and is usually triggered by change in temperature and day length.

TOP LEFT
Male Killifishes are so beautifully coloured and the females so plain they appear to be unrelated. Killies live in rain puddles and temporary pools, and are annuals; that is, they hatch, mature and spawn all in a single wet season. When the puddles dry up, the fish die, but the eggs survive the drought and hatch when rain refills the puddles next year.

TOP RIGHT
The female Dwarf Gourami is a dull silvery colour, while the male at spawning time has brilliant blue spots on a red ground. Like the Siamese Fighter male, he makes a foam nest at the surface in which he suspends the eggs and young. While caring for these he may chase and kill his mate if she cannot escape.

BOTTOM LEFT
Outside the breeding season Black Ruby Barbs of both sexes are yellowish with three or four black bars. At spawning time the male's head becomes a magnificent crimson, his back velvety, and green spots gleam on his flanks.

BOTTOM RIGHT
Among the Cichlids that live in the Great Lakes of Africa, only the dominant males in a shoal achieve the full dark coloration; subordinate males are coloured like the females. Females of the Lake Malawi (Nyasa) Golden Cichlid are a handsome yellow with black and pale blue stripes. Occasionally they assume the black belly of the male, but for what reason is not clear.

Visual Signals

The small active diurnal fishes are 'eye-animals'; they express themselves visually by using colours, fin-gestures and varying postures. We, too, are eye-animals, so we are specially able to appreciate the colourful displays and other visual signals by which fishes indicate their intentions and emotions.

TOP LEFT
The male Guppy in courtship display dances in front of the female with his dorsal fin raised, presenting his colours to her as conspicuously as he can.

BOTTOM LEFT
Many small Damselfishes are highly coloured and very territorial, attacking with great ferocity not only their own kind but almost anything that swims past. However, almost as many Damsels are less colourful, not to say drab; but these dull-looking fish are just as fiercely territorial as their brightly-coloured relatives. Therefore a dull colour does not necessarily denote a retiring disposition, although bright colours generally mean the wearer is aggressive, at least to its own kind.

ABOVE
The blue, black and white stripes of the Cleaner Wrasse and the way it swims signal to other fishes that it is a cleaner. Any fish wishing to be cleaned of parasites will come to the Cleaner's station and position itself with spread fins and gill covers in an invitation posture. The Sabre-tooth Blenny takes advantage of the Cleaner Wrasse's immunity by mimicking its colours and dance, but instead of grooming the unsuspecting larger fish, bites a small chunk out of it.

BELOW LEFT
A commonly used form of display among fishes, as indeed among all sorts of other animals, is to try to look bigger than one actually is, thus intimidating rivals, deterring predators or enticing females by apparently superior size. The Fringed Filefish raises its 'trigger', spreads its tail-fin and opens its throat flap, appearing nearly half as big again.

ABOVE
Siamese Fighting Fish males spar before an actual fight, spreading their resplendent fins and gill covers to intimidate each other. Normally, among less pugnacious species, such a display by the owner of a territory would be enough to cause any intruding male to depart without further fight. But the Siamese Fighter has been specially bred to fight, not flee.

BELOW RIGHT
Special colour signals are flashed by the female African Mouthbrooder to her young when danger threatens. They respond instinctively by crowding back to her mouth. When she feels their touch around her lips, she takes them into her mouth. After the danger has passed she spits them all out again.

Releasers

Males of several species acquire a bright red throat during the breeding season. This is a simple colour signal which acts as a 'releaser' to other fishes of the same species. It elicits aggression in other males, and attracts females.

LEFT
The male Firemouth Cichlid has flaming red on the throat and jaw. When threatening a rival he faces him and raises his gill-covers to present the maximum danger-signal. Fighting involves tugging at each others mouths. Of these two males, one has had his lips dislocated in a mouth-tugging contest. A fright reaction has caused him to pale rapidly. At the same time he signals submission to the other male by flashing female-like bars and blotches on his flanks. This releases a non-aggressive response in the winning male and restrains him from further attack.

BELOW
The Three-spined Stickleback male reacts aggressively to the threatening red breast of another male. Experiments have shown that the red alone releases attacking behaviour: a male Stickleback will attack the crudest, roughly fish-shape models so long as they are painted red on the underside. Females are silvery and are attracted by the red throat of the male.

Supermales

Among reef fishes, few species show a clear colour-differentiation between males and females. Exceptions can be found among the Parrotfishes and Wrasses. Some species have not just one or two colour phases, but three: a drab female, a drab male and a strikingly vivid, larger male. The brilliantly-coloured male is known as a terminal male or supermale.

ABOVE
Among the Parrotfishes males, females and young may share a similar colour and pattern and mate in a swarm. The occasional male attains a larger size and more brilliant coloration; he becomes a supermale. He uses his brighter colours to attract a single female and to defend his territory from other supermales.

RIGHT
The Bluehead Wrasse can be yellow or it can be blue and green. Yellow-phase Blueheads may be juveniles, mature 5-inch females or males. These mate in a group. A small number of males and even some sex-reversed females continue to grow to about 6 inches, developing blue heads and green bodies and becoming the supermales. Supermales always mate singly with one female.

INDEX